A PECK
OF PEPPER

Peter Piper's Practical Principles of Plain and Perfect Pronunciation

PETER PIPER'S POLITE PREFACE

PETER PIPER Puts Pen to Paper, to Produce his Peerless Production, Proudly Presuming it will Please Princes, Peers, and Parliaments, and Procure him the Praise and Plaudits of their Progeny and POSTERITY, as he can prove it Positively to be a PARAGON, or Playful, Palatable, Proverbial, Panegyrical, Philosophical, Philanthropical Phænomenon of Productions.

A PECK
OF PEPPER

with pictures by
FAITH JAQUES

and a postscript by
BRIAN ALDERSON

Chatto & Windus·London·1974

Published by
Chatto & Windus Ltd
40-42 William IV Street
London WC2

*

Clarke, Irwin & Co Ltd
Toronto

For
POLLY SETON

Illustrations © Faith Jaques 1974

ISBN O 7011 5043 2

Printed in Great Britain by
Colour Reproductions Ltd

Text taken from the copy of *Peter Piper's Practical
Principles of Plain and Perfect Pronunciation*
(London: John Harris 1820. No 8 in Harris's
Cabinet of Amusement and Instruction) in the
Osborne Collection of the Toronto Public
Library, as reproduced in Leonard De Vries's
Flowers of Delight
(London: Dennis Dobson, 1965).

A a

Andrew Airpump ask'd his Aunt her Ailment:
Did Andrew Airpump ask his Aunt her Ailment?
If Andrew Airpump ask'd his Aunt her Ailment,
Where was the Ailment of Andrew Airpump's Aunt?

B b

Billy Button bought a butter'd Biscuit:
Did Billy Button buy a butter'd Biscuit?
If Billy Button bought a butter'd Biscuit,
Where's the butter'd Biscuit Billy Button bought?

C c

Captain Crackskull crack'd a Catchpoll's Cockscomb:
Did Captain Crackskull crack a Catchpoll's Cockscomb?
If Captain Crackskull crack'd a Catchpoll's Cockscomb,
Where's the Catchpoll's Cockscomb Captain Crackskull crack'd?

D d

Davy Dolldrum dream'd he drove a Dragon:
Did Davy Dolldrum dream he drove a Dragon?
If Davy Dolldrum dream'd he drove a Dragon,
Where's the Dragon Davy Dolldrum dream'd he drove?

E e

Enoch Elkrig ate an empty Eggshell:
Did Enoch Elkrig eat an empty Eggshell?
If Enoch Elkrig ate an empty Eggshell,
Where's the empty Eggshell Enoch Elkrig ate?

F f

Francis Fribble figur'd on a Frenchman's Filly:
Did Francis Fribble figure on a Frenchman's Filly?
If Francis Fribble figur'd on a Frenchman's Filly,
Where's the Frenchman's Filly Francis Fribble figur'd on?

G g

Gaffer Gilpin got a Goose and Gander:
Did Gaffer Gilpin get a Goose and Gander?
If Gaffer Gilpin got a Goose and Gander,
Where's the Goose and Gander Gaffer Gilpin got?

H h

Humphrey Hunchback had a Hundred Hedgehogs:
Did Humphrey Hunchback have a Hundred Hedgehogs?
If Humphrey Hunchback had a Hundred Hedgehogs,
Where's the Hundred Hedgehogs Humphrey Hunchback had?

I i

Inigo Impey itch'd for an Indian Image:
Did Inigo Impey itch for an Indian Image?
If Inigo Impey itch'd for an Indian Image,
Where's the Indian Image Inigo Impey itch'd for?

J j

Jumping Jacky jeer'd a jesting Juggler:
Did Jumping Jacky jeer a jesting Juggler?
If Jumping Jacky jeer'd a jesting Juggler,
Where's the jesting Juggler Jumping Jacky jeer'd?

K k

Kimbo Kemble kick'd his Kinsman's Kettle:
Did Kimbo Kemble kick his Kinsman's Kettle?
If Kimbo Kemble kick'd his Kinsman's Kettle,
Where's the Kinsman's Kettle Kimbo Kemble kick'd?

L l

Lanky Lawrence lost his Lass and Lobster:
Did Lanky Lawrence lose his Lass and Lobster?
If Lanky Lawrence lost his Lass and Lobster,
Where are the Lass and Lobster Lanky Lawrence lost?

M m

Matthew Mendlegs miss'd a mangled Monkey:
Did Matthew Mendlegs miss a mangled Monkey?
If Matthew Mendlegs miss'd a mangled Monkey,
Where's the mangled Monkey Matthew Mendlegs miss'd?

N n

Neddy Noodle nipp'd his Neighbour's Nutmegs:
Did Neddy Noodle nip his Neighbour's Nutmegs?
If Neddy Noodle nipp'd his Neighbour's Nutmegs,
Where are the Neighbour's Nutmegs Neddy Noodle nipp'd?

O o

Oliver Oglethorpe ogled an Owl and Oyster:
Did Oliver Oglethorpe ogle an Owl and Oyster?
If Oliver Oglethorpe ogled an Owl and Oyster,
Where are the Owl and Oyster Oliver Oglethorpe ogled?

P p

Peter Piper pick'd a Peck of Pepper:
Did Peter Piper pick a Peck of Pepper?
If Peter Piper pick'd a Peck of Pepper,
Where's the Peck of Pepper Peter Piper pick'd?

Q q

Quixote Quicksight quiz'd a queerish Quidbox:
Did Quixote Quicksight quiz a queerish Quidbox?
If Quixote Quicksight quiz'd a queerish Quidbox,
Where's the queerish Quidbox Quixote Quicksight quiz'd?

R r

Rory Rumpus rode a raw-boned Racer:
Did Rory Rumpus ride a raw-bon'd Racer?
If Rory Rumpus rode a raw-bon'd Racer,
Where's the raw-bon'd Racer Rory Rumpus rode?

S s

Sammy Smellie smelt a Smell of Smallcoal:
Did Sammy Smellie smell a Smell of Smallcoal?
If Sammy Smellie smelt a Smell of Smallcoal,
Where's the Smell of Smallcoal Sammy Smellie smelt?

T t

Tip-Toe Tommy turn'd a Turk for Two-pence:
Did Tip-Toe Tommy turn a Turk for Two-pence?
If Tip-Toe Tommy turn'd a Turk for Two-pence,
Where's the Turk for Two-pence Tip-Toe Tommy turn'd?

U u

Uncle's Usher urg'd an ugly Urchin:
Did Uncle's Usher urge an ugly Urchin?
If Uncle's Usher urg'd an ugly Urchin,
Where's the ugly Urchin Uncle's Usher urg'd?

V v

Villiam Veedon vip'd his Vig and Vaistcoat:
Did Villiam Veedon vipe his Vig and Vaistcoat?
If Villiam Veedon vip'd his Vig and Vaistcoat,
Where are the Vig and Vaistcoat Villiam Veedon vip'd?

W   w

Walter Waddle won a walking Wager:
Did Walter Waddle win a walking Wager?
If Walter Waddle won a walking Wager,
Where's the walking Wager Walter Waddle won?

X x   Y y   Z z

X Y Z have made my Brains to crack-o,
X smokes, Y snuffs, and Z chews tobacco;
Yet oft by XYZ much learning's taught;
But Peter Piper beats them all to nought.

Parenthetical Postscript

Nobody knows very much about Peter Piper and the perky, playful, perfectly pointless patter that he perpetrated upon children in the verses that you have just been reading. Almost certainly his 'principles' were first made up into a book in 1813, but people may well have known some of them before that time. (As you probably recognize, the book takes its title from the most popular rhyme in the series, and one which often crops up in word-games along with such other tongue-twisters as 'The Leith police dismisseth us' and 'Can you solder the soldier's shoulder?'. Quite possibly 'Peter Piper pick'd a peck of pickled pepper' existed on its own long before the book was published and the other rhymes were invented to go with it. That would certainly help to account for the book taking the title that it does and not something like 'Andrew Airpump's Amusing and Artful Aid to Absolutely Accurate Articulation'.)

Published now alongside so many other colourful and clever picture books for children, *Peter Piper* may not seem quite so unusual as it must have done on its first appearance. In 1813 books for children were not particularly plentiful and many of them were severe little volumes designed to teach facts or to show children how to behave properly. There were not a lot of exciting or funny books to be bought, so that when John Harris, the first publisher of *Peter Piper*, took the alphabet and turned it into a series of tongue-twisters, he must have met with a delighted response. (Although one curmudgeonly critic did complain that *Peter Piper* was 'a vile book' because it did away with the old, simple way of teaching the alphabet, and because 'degrading trash' like the rhyme on 'Lanky Lawrence' might lead to name-calling, kicked shins and bloody noses on the school playground!)

A more plausible objection might have been that Peter Piper's verses were hard to understand. The children of 1813 may well have been as baffled as the children of today by the rhymes for Inigo Impey or Tip-toe Tommy, even though they would have been more familiar with 'Catchpoll' (a down-at-heels bailiff) or 'Quidbox' (a tobacco-box). Nobody, however, not even the illustrators, seems to have had much idea why the monkey should be 'mangled' and the word was changed in some later editions to the more sensible 'meddling'.

It is unlikely that John Harris would have worried much about these arguments. His chief care was to produce a book that would look well and that would bring enjoyment to the learning child—an aim that he also fulfilled in other volumes of his famous 'Cabinet of Amusement and Instruction' and in two companion-pieces to *Peter*

Piper: Punctuation Personified, by Mr Stops, and *Marmaduke Multiply's Merry Method of Making Minor Mathematicians*. Like their titles, the words and pictures of these books had a sure appeal to children and this latest re-publication of the 'principles' reflects truly the elements established in his eminently entertaining and elegantly educational enterprise.

BRIAN ALDERSON

PETER PIPER PICK'D A PECK OF PEPPER

Engraved illustration from a hand-coloured edition of *Peter Piper* published by John Harris in 1820, reproduced by courtesy of the Osborne Collection of Early Children's Books, Toronto Public Library.